**Give your child a head start with
PICTURE READERS**

Dear Parent,

Now children as young as preschool age can have the fun and satisfaction of reading a book all on their own.

In every Picture Reader, there are simple words, rebus pictures, and 24 flash cards to cut out and keep. (There is a flash card for every rebus picture plus extra cards for reading practice.) After children listen to each story a couple of times, they will be ready to try it all by themselves.

ISBN 0-439-07761-3

Text copyright © 1997 by Grosset & Dunlap, Inc.
Illustrations copyright © 1997 by Heidi Petach.
All rights reserved.
Published by Scholastic Inc., 555 Broadway, New York, NY 10012,
by arrangement with Grosset & Dunlap, Inc., a member of
The Putnam & Grosset Group.
SCHOLASTIC and associated logos are trademarks and/or registered
trademarks of Scholastic Inc.

12 11 10 9 8 7 6 5 4 3 2 1   8 9/9 0 1 2 3/0

Printed in the U.S.A.   24

First Scholastic printing, November 1998

A PICTURE READER

PIG OUT!

By Portia Aborio
Illustrated by Heidi Petach

SCHOLASTIC INC.

New York Toronto London Auckland Sydney
Mexico City New Delhi Hong Kong

Mama  looked out

the  .

The  was up.

The  were singing

"Let's go on a picnic!"

said Mama .

"Yes!" said Papa .

"Yes!" said the

little .

"We will get

the picnic ."

The little  found

the .

They carried the  into the kitchen.

Then they put in

lots of and ,

and ,

and and .

But was the full?

No!

So they put in

 and , and , and .

But was the full?

No!

"I know what we need,"

said Mama .

And she went

to the .

Soon a

came to the .

What was in the ?

 !

Lots of  !

Now the  was full.

"Off we go!"

said Mama .

But the  family

did not go anywhere.

The  was

too heavy!

"Oh, no!"

said the little .

"We cannot have

a picnic.

What will we do now?"

"I know,"

said Mama .

"We will have

a  party!"

The  family

ate all the 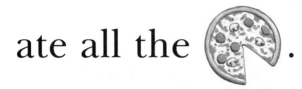 .

And what did they do

with the  and  ,

and  and  ,

and all the other food?

They ate it, of course!